EASA Private Pilot Licence & Light Aircraft Pilot Licence
Aeroplane
Navigation Revision Guide

ISBN 9781906 559632

Airplan Flight Equipment

This book is intended to be a study aid to the Navigation Theoretical Knowledge element of the EASA PPL & LAPL (A) course. It does not in any way replace or overrule the instruction you will receive from a flight instructor at an approved or registered training organisation.

Nothing in this publication overrules or supersedes EASA regulations or EU rules and other documents published by a competent authority; the flight manual/pilot's operating handbook for the aircraft being flown; the pilot order book or operations manual; training syllabus; or the general provisions of good airmanship and safe flying practice.

First Edition 2013

Revised edition 2015

This Revised Edition 2017

©Copyright 2013, 2015 & 2017 AFE Ltd.

EASA Private Pilot Licence & Light Aircraft Pilot Licence
Aeroplane
Navigation Revision Guide

ISBN 9781906 559632

Airplan Flight Equipment
1a Ringway Trading Estate
Shadowmoss Road
Manchester M22 5LH
Tel: 0161 499 0023
Fax: 0161 499 0298
www.afeonline.com

CONTENTS

Intentionally Left Blank

The Solar System

Because of the earth's rotation, the sun appears to 'rise' in the east and 'set' in the west. Because the earth is tilted on its axis, the sun 'rises' to a different height in the sky on each day of the year, reaching its highest midday point during the summer equinox and its lowest midday point during the winter equinox. The tilt of the earth on its axis is responsible for the seasons of the year.

The Earth

Parallels of **latitude** are measured north and south of the equator. Meridians of **longitude** are measured east or west from 0° longitude. A degree of latitude equates to 60 nautical miles, a minute (') of latitude equates to 1 nautical mile.

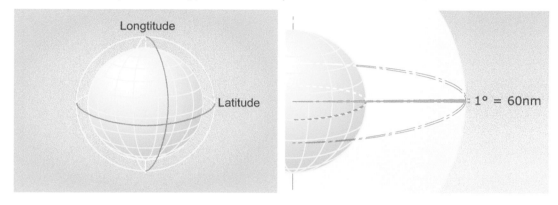

A **small circle** is a line across the surface of the earth whose plane does not pass through the centre of the earth. All parallels of latitude, except the equator, are small circles.

A **great circle** is a line across the surface of the earth whose plane passes through the centre of the earth. All meridians of longitude are great circles.

A **rhumb line** is a line across the surface of the earth which crosses all meridians of longitude at the same angle. All parallels of latitude are rhumb lines.

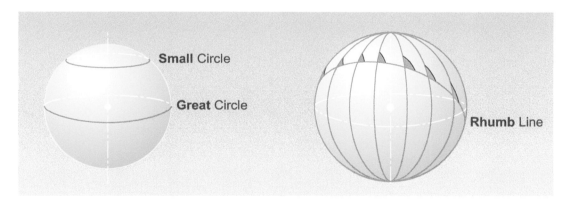

Time

Universal Co-ordinated Time (UTC) is a world standard time which does not vary with location or season. When it is 1400UTC in London, it is 1400UTC all over the world. All other time standards can be defined as a 'difference' from UTC.

Local Mean Time (LMT) is a solar time based on the apparent passage of the sun over a specific location. LMT can be calculated using a location's longitude. For every degree (°) of longitude means a difference between UTC and LMT of 4 minutes. For every 15 minutes (') of arc of longitude the difference is 1 minute of time. At West longitudes, LMT is earlier than UTC; at East longitudes, LMT is later than UTC.

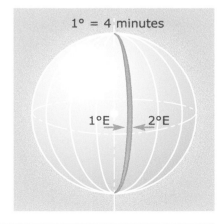

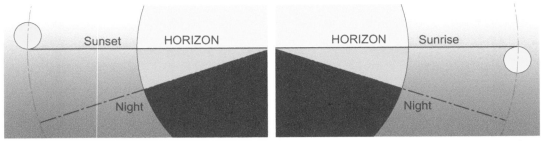

Sunrise can be defined as the moment when the upper edge of the 'rising' sun touches the horizon, **sunset** can be defined as the moment when the upper edge of the 'descending' sun touches the horizon.

Twilight is the period before sunrise, or after sunset, when daylight should still exist. Morning civil twilight starts when the centre of the sun is six degrees below the horizon until sunrise, evening civil twilight starts at sunset and lasts until the centre of the sun is six degrees below the horizon.

Regardless of actual sunrise or sunset time, daylight can be shortened by conditions such as thick cloud or fog, or locations such as in a deep valley.

Directions

Compass Deviation is the error induced in a compass by the local magnetic fields of the aircraft. **Magnetic Variation** is a measure of the difference between true north and magnetic north, caused by the earth's magnetic field.

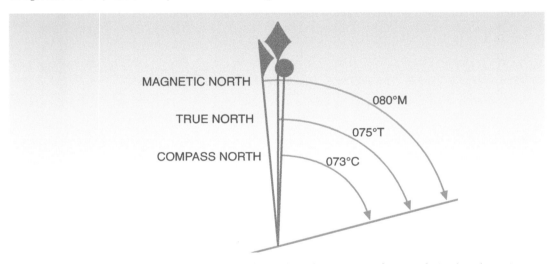

True north is the direction to the actual north pole. **Magnetic north** is the direction to the magnetic north pole. **Compass north** is the direction of north as measured by a compass.

[Diagram PPL Revision Navigation page 6 middle diagram]

True direction corrected for **variation** gives **magnetic direction**. Correcting this for **deviation** gives **compass direction.**

True direction ± **V**ariation = **M**agnetic direction ± **D**eviation = **C**ompass direction
        T   V   **M**   D   **C**

Westerly variation and deviation is added

Easterly variation and deviation is subtracted

Distance

The **nautical mile (nm)** is the most common unit for distance for navigation.

1 Nautical Mile = 1.15 Statute Miles = 1.85 Kilometres

One degree of latitude is always equivalent to 60nm, 1 minute (') of latitude is always equivalent to 1nm.

Magnetism and the Compass

The earth's magnetic field lies almost horizontal to the surface at the equator, and dips to be almost vertical over the magnetic poles.

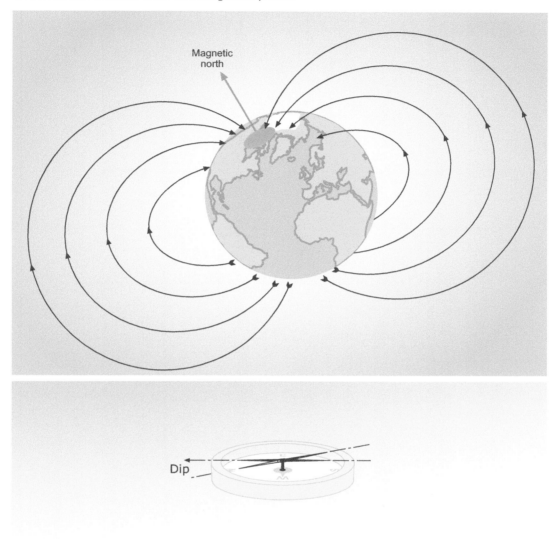

The magnetic needle of a compass will try to align with the earth's magnetic field. As latitude increases, the angle of **dip** of the magnetic needle will increase; the greater the angle of dip, the less accurate the compass will become.

Charts

The standard chart projection for aeronautical charts is the **Lambert** projection. A straight line drawn on a Lambert chart is a great circle – the shortest distance between two points.

Aeronautical charts covering a small area may use a **Mercator** projection. A straight line drawn on a Mercator chart is a rhumb line.

Chart scale is described as a representative fraction – for example 1:500 000. This means that one unit of distance on the chart is equivalent to 500 000 units on the earth.

Most aeronautical charts use standard symbols to depict aeronautical features:

DR Navigation

Deduced Reckoning (usually known as Dead Reckoning) is a navigational technique of estimating position based on a known position 'fix', and then projecting forward from that position based on time flown whilst maintaining an estimated course and groundspeed.

Use of the Navigational Computer

Example, given a true airspeed of 100 knots, a wind velocity of 230° at 20 knots (W/V 230/20) and a track of 170° (all directions are true), find the required true heading to maintain track and the resulting groundspeed.

Wind up method

Step 1 Place the wind direction under the 'INDEX', place the centre dot on the wind speed on the wind grid, and make a mark at the top of the wind grid.

Step 2 Place the track direction under the 'INDEX', place the wind mark on the true airspeed. The wind mark is 10° right of the centre line. 10° right of the index mark indicates a required heading to maintain track – 180° (170 + 10). The centre dot represents the resulting ground speed – 89 knots.

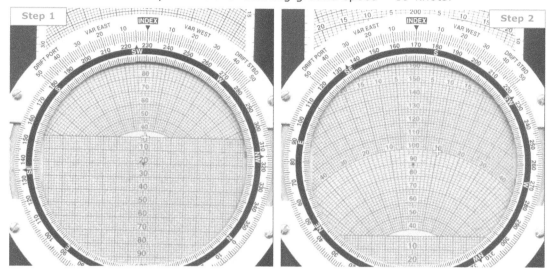

Wind down method

Step 1 Place the wind direction under the 'INDEX', place the centre dot at the top of the wind grid, and make a mark below it at the wind speed.

Step 2 Place the track direction under the 'INDEX', place the centre dot on the true airspeed. The wind mark is 11° left of the centre line.

Step 3 Rotate the plotting disc 11° to the left – bringing the wind mark down. The heading at the INDEX mark (181) is now 11° different to the track, but the wind mark is now only 10° to the left of the centre line. Move the plotting disc back 1° so that the difference in degrees between track and heading is the same both at the 'INDEX' mark and between the wind mark and the centre line.

At the 'INDEX' mark read-off the required heading (180°). At the wind mark read-off the resulting groundspeed (89 knots).

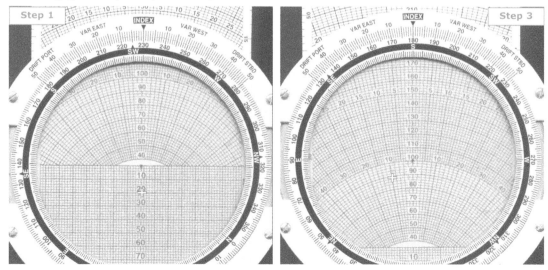

Time and Distance

The circular slide rule side of the flight computer is used for time/speed/distance/fuel calculations. The inner scale represents *time*, and the outer scale represents *distance* or fuel quantity.

On the inner scale there is a 'time index' which represents 60 minutes (ie one hour).

True airspeed is calculated on a mechanical Flight Computer by placing outside air temperature (OAT) against pressure altitude in the airspeed window. True Airspeed (TAS) is then read-off on the outer scale above Calibrated Airspeed (CAS) on the inner scale.

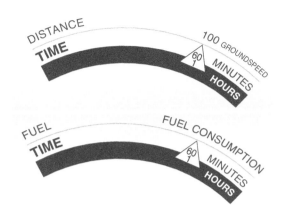

On the conversions side of the flight computer, given the flight time and the fuel consumption, **fuel quantity** is read on the outer scale and time on the inner scale.

To find fuel weight (mass) given a volume and **specific gravity**, on the conversions side of the mechanical Flight Computer, set volume under the appropriate mark for the units being used (ie litres, imperial gallons or US gallons), and under the specific gravity (either in Lbs or Kg) read-off fuel weight (mass).

Example, to find the weight of 100 imperial gallons of AVGAS given a specific gravity of 0.72:

Step 1 Place 100 on the inner scale under 'IMP GAL' on the outer scale

Step 2 Under '72' on the Sp G. lbs scale, locate 72lbs on the inner scale

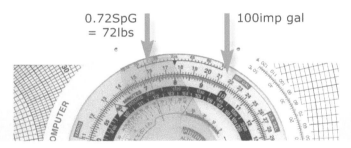

0.72SpG
= 72lbs

100imp gal

The Triangle of Velocities

The **triangle of velocities** can be viewed as a diagram for calculating heading and groundspeed, given a course and distance and wind velocity.

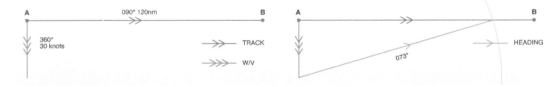

Measurement of Dead Reckoning Elements

Given a distance and time available, the required groundspeed to cover that distance can be calculated using the flight computer, remembering that time is represented on the inner scale and distance on the outer scale.

In-Flight Navigation

Given a heading and groundspeed, True Airspeed and track, the prevailing Wind Velocity (w/v) can be calculated:

Example: Given a TAS of 160 knots, groundspeed 185 knots, heading 320°, and Track (or Track Made Good – TMG) of 330°, what is the w/v?

Wind Down Method

Step 1 Place the centre point over the TAS (160), set the heading (320) under the Index.

Step 2 At a point 10° to the right of heading (ie right drift) make a mark on the ground speed arc (185).

Step 3 Bring the centre point down to the wind component grid, and rotate the plotting disc until the wind mark is directly under the centre point.

Step 4 Read off wind direction under the Index 195°, and wind strength on the wind component grid – 39 knots.

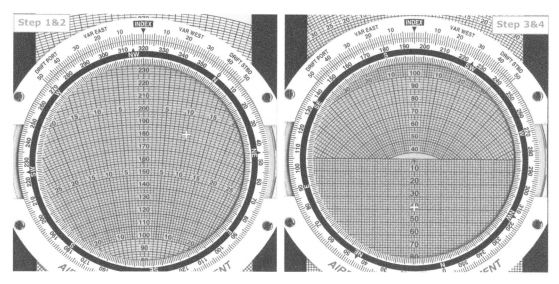

Wind Up Method

Step 1 Place the centre point over the groundspeed (185), set the TMG (330) under the Index.

Step 2 The aircraft is experiencing right drift (10°),so make a mark on the TAS arc (160) 10° to the left of the centre line.

Step 3 Rotate the rotating disc until the wind mark is directly over the centre point, and move the slide until the wind mark is at the top of the grid.

Step 4 Read off wind direction under the Index 195°, and wind strength at the centre point on the wind component grid - 39 knots.

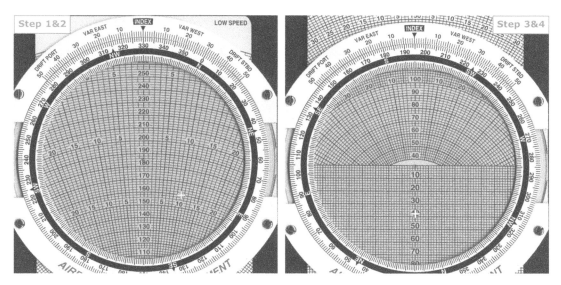

Off-Track Corrections can be calculated using the One in Sixty rule:

$$\frac{\text{Distance off-track (in nm)}}{\text{Distance travelled (in nm)}} \times 60 = \textbf{Track Error (TE)} \text{ in degrees}$$

$$\frac{\text{Distance off-track (in nm)}}{\text{Distance to go (in nm)}} \times 60 = \textbf{Closing Angle (CA)} \text{ in degrees}$$

Total heading correction to reach destination = TE + CA.

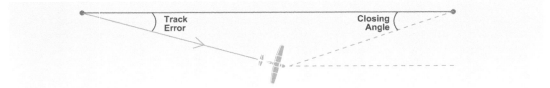

Radio Navigation

The **VHF band** is used for Direction Finding (DF) and VHF Omni Range (VOR)

The **UHF band** is used for Distance Measuring Equipment (DME)

VHF bands and higher operate on the 'line of sight' principle, the higher the station, the greater its range. The VHF band is largely free of interference, although signal accuracy can be affected by site and propagation errors.

Ground Direction Finding (DF)

QDM	The aircraft's **magnetic track to** the station – the magnetic heading, if there was no wind, to take the aircraft to the station
QDR	The aircraft's **magnetic track from** the station
QUJ	The aircraft's **true track to** the station.
QTE	The aircraft's **true track from** the station.

Non-Directional Beacons (NDBs) and Automatic Direction Finding (ADF)

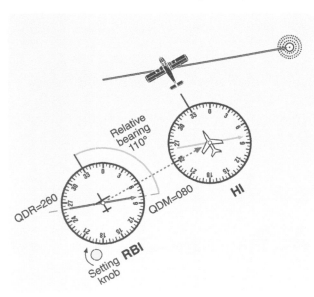

Signals from a **Non-Directional Beacon** (**NDB**) are received by an aircraft receiver called an **Automatic Direction Finder** (**ADF**). The needle of the associated **Relative Bearing Indicator** (**RBI**) points directly to the beacon, showing its direction relative to the aircraft's heading. To convert the RBI direction into a QDM or QDR, the relative bearing must be added or subtracted from the aircraft's magnetic heading.

The promulgated **range of an NDB** is valid by day only, NDB signals can be subject to errors such as coastal refraction, thunderstorm effect and night effect.

VHF Omni Range (VOR)

VHF signals from a **VHF Omni-directional Range** (**VOR**) station are received at the aircraft's VOR receiver and most often displayed on an **Omni Bearing Selector** (**OBS**). When the **Course Deviation Indicator** (**CDI**) needle is centred, the OBS is displaying either the QDM (to), or QDR (from), the VOR station. The 'To/From' ambiguity is resolved by the 'To/From' flag.

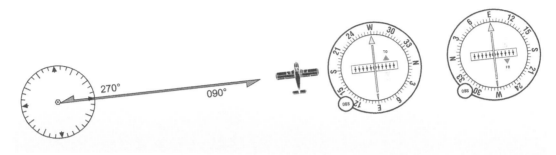

Distance Measuring Equipment (DME)

Distance Measuring Equipment (**DME**) measures and displays the direct distance between the aircraft and the DME station – known as 'slant' range.

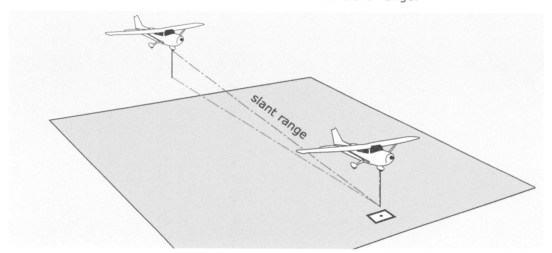

Ground Radar

Radar operates at high radio frequencies and follows the 'line of sight' principle. An object over the horizon, or very close to the ground, may not reflect an echo back to the radar station. The range of radar can be increased by placing it on a high point, and a high-flying aircraft can be 'seen' by radar at a greater range than a low-flying one.

Secondary Surveillance Radar (SSR)

Secondary Surveillance Radar (SSR) can usually detect an aircraft at lower altitudes and greater range than a 'primary' radar unit in the same location. SSR requires a transponder in the aircraft, information from the aircraft's transponder is displayed to an ATC controller on the same screen as primary radar.

GNSS

A global navigation satellite system (**GNSS**) is a satellite navigation system with global coverage. The USA's Global Positioning System (GPS) is one form of GNSS, which requires a satellite 'constellation' and a GNSS receiver.

In order to obtain a three dimensional position fix (level as well as horizontal position), a GNSS receiver must be receiving signals from at least four satellites. If a GNSS receiver can see just three satellites, only two dimensional (horizontal position only) navigation is possible.

Intentionally Left Blank

EASA PPL & LAPL Aeroplane Navigation

Time allowed: 45 minutes

No. of questions: 12

Total Marks: 100

Instructions:

The paper consists of 12 multiple choice questions, each carries 8.33 marks. The pass mark is 75% (ie 9 questions or more must be answered correctly). Marks are not deducted for incorrect answers.

Be sure to carefully read each question and ensure that you understand it before considering the answer choices. Only one of the answers is complete and correct; the others are either incomplete, incorrect or based on a misconception.

You should indicate the correct answer by placing a cross in the appropriate box of the answer sheet. If you decide to change an answer, you should erase the original choice and put a cross in the box representing your new selection.

Each question has an average answer time available of 3 minutes 45 seconds. No credit is given for unanswered questions.

Navigation Practice Paper ONE

GENERAL NAVIGATION SECTION

1. Which of the following statements is true of an aeronautical chart which has a scale of 1:500,000?

    (a) 1cm on the chart represents 500,000km across the earth

    (b) The area of the chart is 500,000km²

    (c) 1 inch on the chart represents 500,000 inches across the earth

    (d) 1 degree of latitude is equal to 500,000 metres

2. An aircraft is maintaining a track of 136°T, with 4° left drift, over an area when variation is 6°E and the compass deviation (from the compass correction card) is 2°W. The aircraft's compass heading is:

    (a) 144°M

    (b) 148°M

    (c) 140°M

    (d) 136°M

3. An aircraft at FL50 at an indicated airspeed (IAS) of 104 knots. If the outside air temperature is +10°C, and ignoring other effects such as instrument and position error, what is the aircraft's true airspeed (TAS)?

    (a) 109kt

    (b) 113kt

    (c) 104kt

    (d) 96kt

4. An aircraft is overhead point A at 1432UTC, maintaining a true airspeed (TAS) of 97kt. Course is set for point B which is 75nm away on a track of 220°T, the forecast w/v is 280/15kt. What is the ETA for B?

    (a) 1523UTC

    (b) 1515UTC

    (c) 1529UTC

    (d) 1534UTC

5. Complete the table below and use it to select the correct magnetic heading and leg time:

PL	ALT/TEMP	CAS	TAS	W/V	TR(T)	HDG(T)	Var	HDG(M)	G/S	DIST	TIME	ETA
	4000/+15°C	95		290/15	025		4°W			47		

    (a) 030°M/32mins

    (b) 025°T/34mins

    (c) 032°M/29mins

    (d) 021°M/28mins

6. What is the meaning of the map symbol below?

    (a) VOR

    (b) Co-located, frequency paired VOR/DME

    (c) TACAN

    (d) VOR, with non frequency-paired DME

7. An aircraft needs to arrive over its destination in not less than 45 minutes – the destination is 75nm away. There is no headwind or tailwind component, the aircraft is at FL70 and the outside air temperature is 0°C. What is the minimum Calibrated Airspeed (CAS) required to arrive at the desired time?

    (a)   101 knots

    (b)   111 knots

    (c)   90 knots

    (d)   107 knots

8. An aircraft fuel tank contains 60 litres of fuel, its average fuel flow is 5 US gallons per hour, what is the 'endurance' without reserves (in other words, to dry tank)?

    (a)   2 hours 55 minutes

    (b)   3 hours 10 minutes

    (c)   2 hours 37 minutes

    (d)   2 hours 48 minutes

9. An aircraft is flying between two points 60nm apart, after 20nm the aircraft is 3nm to the right of track. What heading correction is required to route directly to the destination?

    (a)   4.5° left

    (b)   9° left

    (c)   13.5° right

    (d)   13.5° left

RADIO NAVIGATION SECTION

10. The VOR receiver in an aircraft displays:

    (a)   A magnetic bearing in relation to the VOR station

    (b)   A true bearing from the VOR station

    (c)   A compass bearing from the VOR station

    (d)   The vertical inclination between the aircraft and the VOR station

11. Which of the following radio navigation aids operate in the VHF band?

    (a)   VOR

    (b)   DME

    (c)   GPS

    (d)   NDB

12. An aircraft is located on the 165° radial from a VOR station. In order to track towards the VOR station, with the Course Deviation Indicator (CDI) operating in the natural sense, the Omni Bearing Selector (OBS) should be set to:

    (a)   165°, TO flag

    (b)   165°, FROM flag

    (c)   345°, TO flag

    (d)   345°, FROM flag

GENERAL NAVIGATION SECTION

1. An aircraft is maintaining a heading of 340°C. Compass deviation (from the compass correction card) is 4°E, the local variation is 8°W. If the aircraft is experiencing 5° right drift, the aircraft's true track is:

    (a)   341°T

    (b)   336°T

    (c)   330°M

    (d)   352°T

2. An aircraft at FL70 at an indicated airspeed (IAS) of 97 knots. The outside air temperature is -10°C, ignoring effects such as instrument and position error, what is the aircraft's true airspeed (TAS)?

    (a)   90kt

    (b)   86kt

    (c)   105kt

    (d)   110kt

3. An aircraft is overhead point A at 0812UTC and sets course for point B which is 108nm away on a track of 130°T, the forecast w/v is 020/25kt. If the aircraft maintains a TAS of 115kts, what is the ETA at B?

    (a)   0916UTC

    (b)   0907UTC

    (c)   0928UTC

    (d)   0912UTC

4. Given a TAS of 95 knots, a groundspeed of 102 knots, a heading of 252°T and a track of 264°T, what is the wind velocity?

    (a)   250/20

    (b)   080/15

    (c)   330/25

    (d)   150/22

5. Overhead point A fuel contents are 17 US gallons. 23 minutes later, overhead point B, fuel contents are 14 US gallons. The next waypoint (point C) is 48 minutes away. Assuming fuel flow remains constant, how much fuel (in kg) will remain overhead point C assuming a Specific Gravity (Sp.G) of 0.72?

    (a)   37kg

    (b)   32kg

    (c)   22kg

    (d)   48kg

6. An aircraft is flying between two points 90nm apart, after 30nm the aircraft is 4nm to the left of track. What heading correction is required to route directly to the destination?

    (a)   10° left

    (b)   12° right

    (c)   8°right

    (d)   4°left

7. Choose the phrase which most accurately completes the following sentence.

"The magnetic compass is considered most accurate at......"

(a) the 45°line of latitude

(b) the magnetic poles

(c) high latitudes

(d) low latitudes

8. An aeroplane has a maximum demonstrated crosswind component of 12 knots. If the surface wind speed is 20 knots, what is the maximum difference in degrees between runway direction and wind direction before the maximum demonstrated cross wind component is exceeded?

Assume that both runway direction and wind direction are in degrees magnetic.

(a) 40 degrees

(b) 25 degrees

(c) 60 degrees

(d) 20 degrees

RADIO NAVIGATION SECTION

9. VDF operates in the ....(i).... band and its accuracy may be degraded by ....(ii)....

	(i)	(ii)
(a)	VHF	Night effect
(b)	LF	Site and propagation error
(c)	EHF	Thunderstorm effect
(d)	VHF	Site and propagation error

10. An aircraft is tracking directly away from an NDB on a QDR of 290° and experiencing 10° of port drift. The relative bearing of the NDB as indicated by the needle of the Relative Bearing Indicator (RBI) is:

(a) 170°

(b) 190°

(c) 290°

(d) 280°

11. An aircraft's DME measures the:

(a) Ground distance to a DME station

(b) Route track to a DME station

(c) 'Slant' distance to a DME station

(d) Horizontal distance to a DME station

12. An aircraft is located on the 150° radial of a VOR. If the pilot wishes to track directly towards the VOR, for the Course Deviation Indicator (CDI) to give indications in the correct sense, it should be set to:

(a) 150° FROM

(b) 150° TO

(c) 330° TO

(d) 330° FROM

GENERAL NAVIGATION SECTION

1. In relation to meridians of longitude, which of the following statements is correct?

    (a) Meridians of longitude are measured north or south of the equator

    (b) All meridians of longitude are small circles

    (c) All meridians of longitude are great circles

    (d) Meridians of longitude are measured with reference to magnetic north

2. With regard to daylight:

    (a) Daylight always ends 30 minutes after sunset

    (b) Factors such as deep valleys, dense cloud cover or poor visibility can cause daylight to end earlier than predicted by a sunset table

    (c) Daylight hours can be accurately predicated regardless of weather conditions

    (d) Daylight is defined as the period from 30 minutes after sunrise to 30 minutes before sunset

3. An aircraft is overhead point A at 1754UTC and sets course for point B which is 100nm away on a track of 330°T, the forecast w/v is 240/20kt. If the aircraft maintains a TAS of 110kts, what is the ETA at B?

    (a) 1900UTC

    (b) 1855UTC

    (c) 1850UTC

    (d) 1845UTC

4. Overhead waypoint A fuel contents are 48kg. 37 minutes later, overhead waypoint B, fuel contents are 40kg. The next waypoint (C) is 23 minutes away. Assuming fuel flow remains constant, how much fuel (in US gallons) will remain overhead C assuming a Specific Gravity (Sp.G) of 0.72?

    (a) 9.6 US gallons

    (b) 10.7 US gallons

    (c) 11.3 US gallons

    (d) 12.8 US gallons

5. An aircraft is flying between two points 100nm apart, after 20nm the aircraft is 2nm to the left of track. What heading correction is required to route directly to the destination?

    (a) 12° left

    (b) 11° right

    (c) 7.5° right

    (d) 4° left

6. As latitude increases towards the magnetic pole, 'dip' becomes ....(i)........ and compass errors become ....(ii)......... . The missing words are:

    (ii)

    (a) Greater   Lesser

    (b) Greater   Greater

    (c) Lesser   Greater

    (d) Lesser   Lesser

7. An aircraft is cruising at Flight Level (FL) 75, the correct QNH is 993hpa. If the terrain directly below the aircraft is 1400ft AMSL, assuming 1hPa = 30ft and ignoring any temperature correction, what is:

(i) The aircraft's altitude

(ii) The aircraft's height

	(i)	(ii)
(a)	6900ft	5500ft
(b)	8100ft	6700ft
(c)	6700ft	8100ft
(d)	5500ft	6900ft

RADIO NAVIGATION SECTION

8. In order to obtain a three dimensional position fix (that is, a vertical position as well as a horizontal position), a GPS (GNSS) receiver must be receiving signals from at least how many satellites?

(a) 3

(b) 4

(c) 1

(d) 6

9. A QUJ [i] and a QDM [ii] are best described as follows:

	[i]	[ii]
(a)	A true track to a station	A true track from a station
(b)	A true track from a station	A true track to a station
(c)	A magnetic track to a station	A magnetic track from a station
(d)	A true track to a station	A magnetic track to a station

10. An aircraft is tracking directly away from a Non Directional Beacon (NDB) maintaining a track of 050°, whilst experiencing 10° starboard drift. Under these circumstances, the nose of the needle of a Relative Bearing Indicator (RBI) will indicate a relative bearing to the NDB of:

(a) 190°

(b) 170°

(c) 240°

(d) 220°

11. Which of the following radio navigation aids operate in the VHF band?

(a) VDF and VOR

(b) SSR and DME

(c) NDB and GPS

(d) NDB and VOR

12. The particular item of aircraft radio navigation equipment which measures the phase difference between two signals from a ground station is a:

(a) Secondary Surveillance Radar (SSR)

(b) VHF Omni-directional Range (VOR)

(c) Distance Measuring Equipment (DME)

(d) Global Positioning System (GPS)

Navigation paper 1 Q1 Answer C

A scale can be described as a 'representative fraction', so the scale 1:500,000 means that any unit of distance (inches, miles, thumbs, whatever) on the chart represents a distance 500,000 times longer across the earth itself.

Further Reference: PPL3 Navigation > Aeronautical Maps > Scale and Distance

Navigation paper 1 Q2 Answer D

Questions of this type regarding heading calculation can be tackled by applying two basic principles:

1 True direction ± **Variation** = **Magnetic** direction ± **Deviation** = **Compass** direction
     T   **V**   **M**   **D**   **C**

2 Easterly variation or deviation is **deducted** from heading
Westerly variation or deviation is **added** to heading
East is **Least, West** is **Best**

With this guide, it is often easiest to construct a table to perform the required calculation:

True Direction	Variation	Magnetic Direction	Deviation	Compass Direction
T	V	M	D	C

In the question, it is first necessary to calculate that if the aircraft is tracking 136°, with 4°of left drift, its heading is 140°.

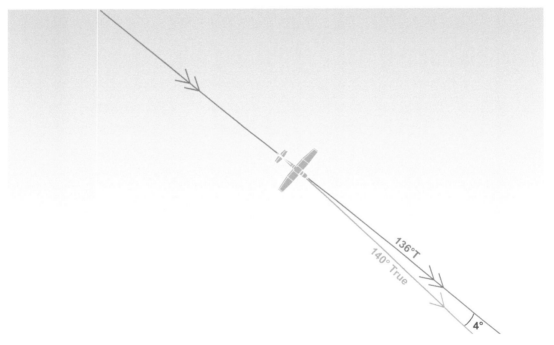

The table can then be completed:

Heading	Variation	Magnetic Heading	Deviation	Compass Heading
T	V	M	D	C
140°T	-6°E	134°M	+2°W	136°M

Further Reference: PPL3 Navigation > Aeronautical Maps > Measurement of Direction

Navigation paper 1 Q3 Answer B

The calculation of true airspeed is most easily accomplished using a flight computer. If using a 'mechanical' flight computer, when the outside air temperature (+10°C) is placed against the pressure altitude (5000ft) in the 'airspeed' window, above the IAS (104) on the inner scale, the TAS (113) is read-off on the outer scale.

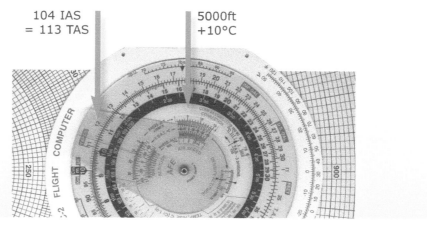

104 IAS = 113 TAS

5000ft +10°C

Further Reference: PPL3 Navigation > Navigation Principles: Airspeed, Groundspeed, Time and Distance > Airspeed

Navigation paper 1 Q4 Answer A

The first stage in answering this question is to calculate groundspeed.

A mental check indicates that as there an element of headwind; the w/v is 60° off the track, so the headwind component is about 50% of the windspeed (hence about 7.5 knots) making a groundspeed of around 90 knots

When the TAS, track and w/v are placed into a flight computer, the resulting groundspeed is calculated at 88 knots, which is in accordance with the mental check.

Using a 'mechanical' flight computer, if the groundspeed (88) is placed over the time index, below the distance (75nm) on the outer scale, the time (51 mins) is read-off on the inner scale. 1432UTC + 51 minutes = 1523UTC.

Further Reference: PPL3 Navigation > Navigation Principles: The Triangle of Velocities > Triangle of Velocities Calculations on the Flight Computer
and
Navigation Principles: Airspeed, Groundspeed, Time and Distance > Time, Speed and Distance

Navigation paper 1 Q5 Answer D

The completed table should look like this:

PL ALT/TEMP	CAS	TAS	W/V	TR(T)	HDG(T)	Var	HDG(M)	G/S	DIST	TIME	ETA
4000/+15°C	95	102	290/15	025	017	4°W	021	102	47	28	

A mental check should confirm that the aircraft's heading will be to the left of track (into the wind) and because the wind is at around 90° to track, the ground speed will be close to TAS.

From the completed table, the magnetic heading (021°M) and leg time (or time en-route) of 28 minutes is taken.

Further Reference: PPL3 Navigation > Navigation Principles: The Triangle of Velocities > Triangle of Velocities Calculations on the Flight Computer
and
Navigation Principles: Airspeed, Groundspeed, Time and Distance > Time, Speed and Distance

Navigation paper 1 Q6 Answer B

The ICAO chart symbols for the various radionavigation aids can be found on the chart key.

Further Reference: PPL3 Navigation > Radio Navigation > Distance Measuring Equipment (DME)

Answers ONE

Navigation paper 1 Q7 Answer C

Using the flight computer, by placing time (45 minutes) under distance (75nm), the required groundspeed can be read-off above the time index – 100 knots. Because there is no headwind or tailwind component, groundspeed = TAS.

Now, in the airspeed window, place the air temperature (0°C) against the pressure altitude (7000ft) and underneath TAS (100knots) on the outer scale, read CAS on the inner scale – 90 knots

Further Reference: Navigation Principles: Airspeed, Groundspeed, Time and Distance >
                       Time, Speed and Distance

Navigation paper 1 Q8 Answer B

On a flight computer, 5 US gallons per hour converts into 19 litres per hour. Placing the time index under fuel consumption (19) – ie 19 litres per hour. Under the fuel amount (60 litres) on the outer scale, time to use all the fuel can be read-off on the inner scale – 3 hours and 10 minutes

3hr 10min  19Ltr per hr

Further Reference: PPL3 Navigation > Flight Planning: Fuel Planning > Fuel Planning

Navigation paper 1 Q9 Answer D

Using the 'One in Sixty' rule, on a flight computer the distance off track (3nm) is placed over the distance flown (20nm), above the '60'.index on the inner scale the track error is read-off on the outer scale (9°).

9° 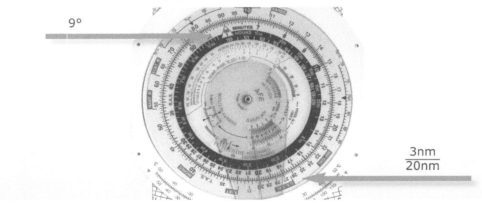 $\frac{3nm}{20nm}$

If heading is altered to the left by the amount of track error, the aircraft will merely parallel the required track.

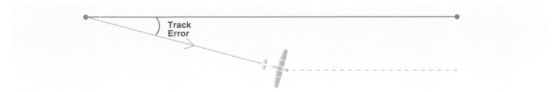

Track
Error

The closing angle is found by placing distance off-track (3nm) over distance to go (40nm), above the '60' index on the inner scale a closing angle of 4.5° is read-off.

$\frac{3nm}{40nm}$ 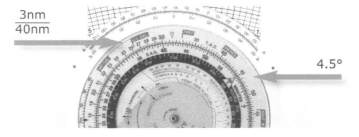 4.5°

Therefore, the total heading correction required is Track Error (TE) of 9° + Closing Angle (CA) of 4.5° = 13.5° Left

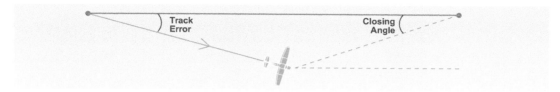

Further Reference: PPL3 Navigation > Off-Track Calculations and Track Marking > The One in Sixty Rule

Navigation paper 1 Q10 Answer A

The VOR station transmits a signal which is referenced to magnetic north, the VOR receiver displays this signal in the form of a magnetic bearing to or from the VOR station.

Those with a pedantic frame of mind will want to know that the VOR bearing is based on magnetic north at the VOR station, not at the aircraft.

Further Reference: PPL3 Navigation > Radio Navigation > VHF Omni-directional Range (VOR)

Navigation paper 1 Q11 Answer A

This can be remembered simply by knowing what the abbreviation 'VOR' stands for, namely:

VHF **O**mni-directional **R**ange (VOR)

Further Reference: PPL3 > Navigation > Radio Navigation > VHF Omni-directional Range

Navigation paper 1 Q12 Answer C

If the aircraft is located on the 165° radial, it is on a bearing of 165° FROM the VOR station.

In order to track directly towards the VOR station the aircraft needs to fly the reciprocal course directly towards the station. 165° + 180° = 345°. For the CDI needle to operate in the correct sense (ie show correct 'fly left' or 'fly right' indications), the 'TO' flag must be showing when tracking towards the station.

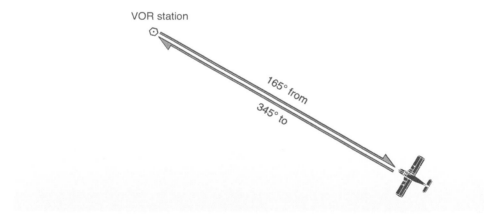

Further Reference: PPL3 > Navigation > Radio Navigation > VHF Omni-directional Range (VOR)

Navigation paper 2 Q1 Answer A

This question can be best answered using a table for calculating direction, remembering that Easterly corrections are deducted, Westerly corrections are added:

True Heading T	Variation V	Magnetic Heading M	Deviation D	Compass Heading C
336°T	8°W	344°M	4°E	340°C

The true direction calculated is the aircraft's heading. The question requires the aircraft's track to be calculated. If an aircraft is heading 336°T with 5° of right drift, its track is 341°T.

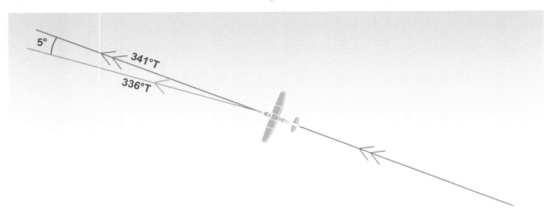

PPL3 Navigation > Aeronautical Maps > Measurement of Direction

Navigation paper 2 Q2 Answer C

The calculation of true airspeed is most easily accomplished using a flight computer. Using a 'mechanical' flight computer, if the outside air temperature (-10°C) is placed against the pressure altitude (7000ft) in the 'airspeed' window, the TAS (105) is read-off on the outer scale above the IAS.

Further Reference: PPL3 Navigation > Navigation Principles: Airspeed, Groundspeed, Time and Distance > Airspeed

Navigation paper 2 Q3 Answer B

The first stage in answering this question is to calculate groundspeed.

A mental check indicates that there an element of tailwind; the w/v is 110° off the track, so the tailwind component is about 30% of the windspeed (hence about 7.5 knots) making a groundspeed of around 123 knots

When the TAS, track and w/v are placed into a flight computer, the resulting groundspeed is calculated at 119 knots, which is in accordance with the mental check.

Using a 'mechanical' flight computer, if the time index (60 minutes) is placed under the groundspeed (119kt), below the distance (108nm) on the outer scale, the time (55 mins) is read-off on the inner scale. 0812UTC + 55 minutes = 0907UTC.

Further Reference: PPL3 Navigation > Navigation Principles: The Triangle of Velocities > Triangle of Velocities Calculations on the Flight Computer
and
Navigation Principles: Airspeed, Groundspeed, Time and Distance > Time, Speed and Distance

Navigation paper 2 Q4 Answer D

A mental check shows that there is an element of tailwind (7 knots) and that the wind must be coming from the left of the aircraft's heading.

By placing the parameters given into the question into the flight computer, a wind velocity (w/v) of 150°T at 22 knots is calculated. This accords with the mental check.

Further Reference: PPL3 Navigation > Navigation Principles: The Triangle of Velocities > Triangle of Velocities Calculations on the Flight Computer

Navigation paper 2 Q5 Answer C

On a flight computer, placing time between A and B (23 minutes) under fuel used between A and B (3 US gallons) gives a fuel consumption (above the time index) of 7.5 US gallons in an hour.

Fuel contents overhead B are 14 US gallons, at the fuel consumption of 7.5 US gallons/hour, the further 48 minutes to overhead C will consume a further 6 US gallons.

Therefore, overhead C the fuel contents will be 8 US gallons (14 – 6).

7.5US Gal/hr

6US Gal

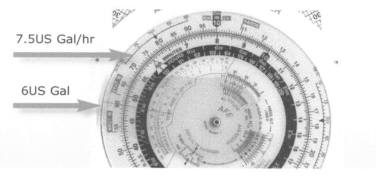

At a specific gravity of 0.72, 8 US gallons weighs 22kg.

Further Reference: PPL3 Navigation > Flight Planning: Fuel Planning > Fuel Planning
and
PPL3 Navigation > Flight Planning: Fuel Planning > Specific
Gravity Calculation

Navigation paper 2 Q6 Answer B

Using the 'One in Sixty' rule, on a flight computer the distance off track (4nm) is placed over the distance flown (30nm), above the '60' index on the inner scale the track error is read-off on the outer scale (8°).

The closing angle is found by placing distance off-track (4nm) over distance to go (60nm), above the '60' index on the inner scale a closing angle of 4° is read-off.

Therefore, the total heading correction required is Track Error (TE) of 8° + Closing Angle (CA) of 4° = 12° right

PPL3 Navigation > Off-Track Calculations and Track Marking > The One in Sixty Rule

Answers TWO

Navigation paper 2 Q7 Answer D

Disregarding magnetised objects around the compass, the needle of magnetic compass tries to align itself with the earth's magnetic field. This field is almost horizontal over the magnetic equator, and almost vertical over a magnetic pole.

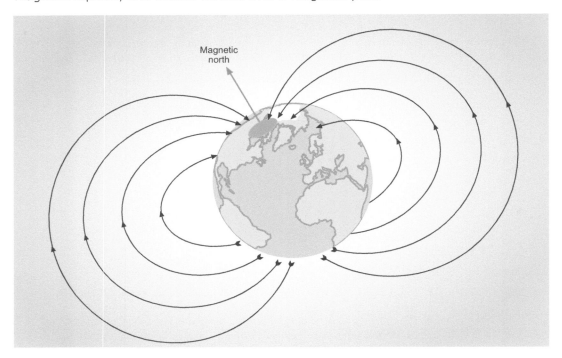

As the needle of the magnetic compass is pulled down by the earth's magnetic field, a component known as 'dip' (abbreviated to 'Z') occurs. The closer the compass is to a magnetic pole, the greater the dip and the more pronounced the compass error.

It follows that is 'low' latitudes (near the equator), where dip is least, the magnetic compass will be at its most accurate.

Further Reference: PPL4 Aircraft General Knowledge > Instruments > The Magnetic Compass

Navigation paper 2 Q8 Answer A

As a mental check, crosswind component can be calculated using a number of 'rules of thumb'. For example, at a 30 degrees angle between runway direction and wind direction, the crosswind component is about half the wind speed (so in this case, half 20 knots = 10 knots). At a 60 degrees angle between runway direction and wind direction, the crosswind component is about the full wind speed (so in this case, 20 knots). Therefore, as a mental check at 20 knots wind speed, a cross wind component of 12 knots will be reached at slightly more than 30 degrees difference between runway direction and wind direction, but much less than 60 degrees. 40 degrees off would be a rational mental check figure, given that most 'rules-of-thumb' estimate that at 40 degrees difference between runway direction and wind direction, the cross wind component is around 2/3rds of wind strength.

To get a more precise figure, use the 'plotting disc' side of a flight computer. Set the direction to 000 degrees for simplicity, place the 'centre dot' on the top of the 'wind grid' (0 knots) and make a mark directly below the centre dot at 20 knots ('wind down' method). If using the 'wind up' method, place the centre dot on the 20 knot line of the wind grid and then make a mark directly above it on the top line of the wind grid (0 knots).

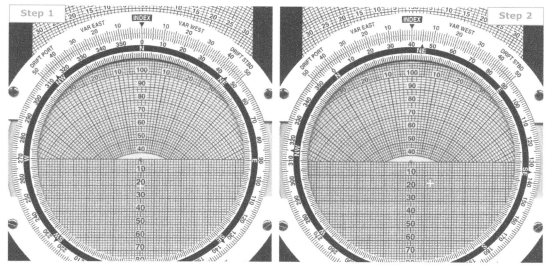

With either method, now rotate the plotting disc until the mark you have made reaches the '12 knots' vertical line on the wind grid. The difference in degrees at the top of the plotting disc is the difference in runway direction and wind direction that produces a 12 knots cross wind component – in this case 40 degrees.

Further Reference: PPL3 > Navigation > Flight Planning: Performance > Cross wind Component

Navigation paper 2 Q9 Answer D

VDF operates in the Very High Frequency (VHF) band (30-300MHz) – in fact VDF stands for VHF Direction Finding.

VHF transmissions are largely unaffected by errors (eg coastal refraction, thunderstorm effect, night effect etc.) that effect transmissions in the lower frequency bands. However, VHF transmissions can be affected by three particular errors:

- Site error, if the area around the transmission area contains buildings or obstacles which can reflect or deflect signals.

- Propagation error, (also sometimes known as 'scalloping'), caused if the signal is travelling over hilly terrain and the receiver is at low level – the signal can be deflected or scattered.

- Duct propagation, when a strong temperature inversion causes VHF signals to travel far further at low level than the normal 'line-of-site' range limitation.

Further Reference: PPL3 > Navigation > Radio Navigation > VHF Omni-directional
                      Range
                      and
                      PPL3 > Navigation > Radio Navigation > Ground Direction
                      Finding (DF)

Navigation paper 2 Q10 Answer A

First consider the situation if there was no drift. The aircraft is tracking directly away from the NDB, so regardless of the QDR (radial), the needle of the Relative Bearing Indicator (RBI) will point directly behind the aircraft, ie to 180°. Remember, the question is asking about the <u>relative</u> bearing indication – where the NDB is located relative to the nose of the aircraft (which is taken as 000°).

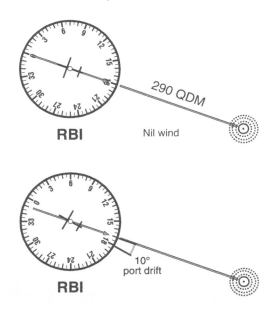

The key point then is the drift. If the aircraft is drifting port (left) by 10°, the aircraft nose must be pointing 10° to the right of track. If this situation is depicted over the RBI, you can see that the needle is pointing 10° to the right of 180°, namely 170°.

Further Reference: PPL3 > Navigation > Radio Navigation > Automatic Direction
                       Finding (ADF)

Navigation paper 2 Q11 Answer C

The aircraft's DME uses radar principles (measuring the time taken for a radio pulse to be sent and returned back to the aircraft) to measure the direct distance between the aircraft and the DME ground station. Anytime the aircraft is higher than the DME ground station, this distance will be the direct 'slant' range to the DME, not the exact horizontal distance to overhead the ground DME. At lower altitudes (below 10,000ft) and anything more than a few miles from the ground DME station, the difference between horizontal range and slant range is normally immaterial.

Further Reference: PPL3 > Navigation > Radio Navigation > Distance Measuring
                       Equipment (DME)

Navigation paper 2 Q12 Answer C

The aircraft is on the 150° radial – by definition a radial is a magnetic direction <u>FROM</u> a station. This situation is depicted below:

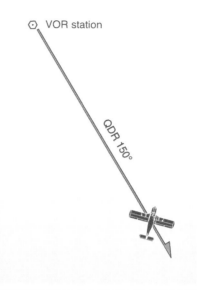

In order to fly <u>TO</u> the station, the aircraft must fly in the reciprocal (opposite) direction to the radial – in this case 330° (ie 150° + 180°).

On the Course Deviation Indicator (CDI) this is achieved by setting the desired track at the top of the indicator, and – most essentially – checking that the 'TO' flag is showing.

When using a VOR (or localiser or ILS), the recommended sequence of actions is **FIFO**:

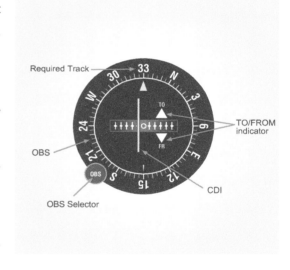

Frequency – check and select

Ident – identify the morse code

Flags – check that the warning flag has disappeared

OBS – use the Omni Bearing Selector (OBS) to select the desired track and check that the TO/FROM flag appears in the correct sense.

Further Reference: PPL3 > Navigation > Radio Navigation > VHF Omni-directional Range

Answers TWO

Navigation paper 3 Q1 Answer C

All meridians of longitude are semi-circles whose plane passes through the centre of the earth. A line across the surface of the earth whose plane passes through the centre of the earth is a great circle.

Further Reference: PPL3 Navigation > The Earth > Lines on the Surface of the Earth

Navigation paper 3 Q2 Answer B

Daylight is the period during which the surface is illuminated by direct or indirect sunlight. It follows that any situation which reduces the sun's illumination – such as dense cloud cover, or poor visibility (such as fog), or high ground blocking out the sun, or any combination of these factors, can markedly reduce daylight. If such a situation occurs an when the sun is close to or below the horizon; it can reduce illumination sufficiently that daylight no longer exists even, if the technical definition of night does not apply.

Further Reference: PPL3 Navigation > Flight Planning: Time > Sunrise and Sunset

Navigation paper 3 Q3 Answer C

The first stage in answering this question is to calculate groundspeed.

A mental check indicates that the wind is at 90° to the track, so and head or tailwind component is likely to be very small.

When the TAS, track and w/v are placed into a flight computer, the resulting groundspeed is calculated at 108 knots, which is in accordance with the mental check.

Using a 'mechanical' flight computer, if the groundspeed (108kt) is placed over the time index, below the distance (100nm) on the outer scale, the time (56 mins to the nearest minute) is read-off on the inner scale. 1754UTC + 56 minutes = 1850UTC.

Further Reference: PPL3 Navigation > Navigation Principles: The Triangle of Velocities > Triangle of Velocities Calculations on the Flight Computer
and
Navigation Principles: Airspeed, Groundspeed, Time and Distance > Time, Speed and Distance

Navigation paper 3 Q4 Answer D

On a flight computer, placing time between A and B (37minutes) over fuel used between A and B (8kg) gives a fuel consumption (above the time index) of 13kg per hour.

Fuel contents overhead B are 40kg, at the fuel consumption of 13kg/hour, the further 23 minutes to overhead C will consume a further 5kg so fuel contents overhead C will be 35kg.

At a specific gravity of 0.72, 35kg of fuel is equivalent to 12.8 US gallons.

23min $\dfrac{0.72\text{SpG}}{35\text{kg}}$

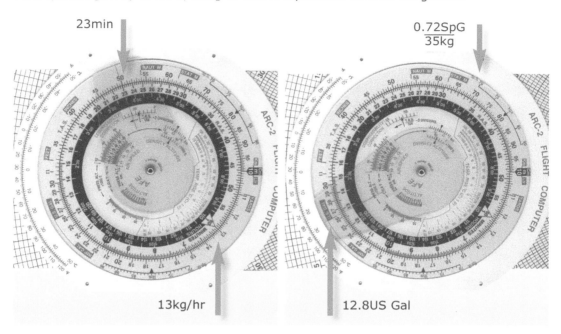

13kg/hr   12.8US Gal

Further Reference: PPL3 Navigation > Flight Planning: Fuel Planning > Fuel Planning and
PPL3 Navigation > Flight Planning: Fuel Planning > Specific Gravity Calculation

Navigation paper 3 Q5 Answer C

Using the 'One in Sixty' rule, on a flight computer the distance off track (2nm) is placed over the distance flown (20nm), above the '60'.index on the inner scale the track error is read-off on the outer scale (6°).

The closing angle is found by placing distance off-track (2nm) over distance to go (80nm), above the '60' index on the inner scale a closing angle of 1.5° is read-off.

Therefore, the total heading correction required is Track Error (TE) of 6° + Closing Angle (CA) of 1.5° = 7.5° right

Further Reference: PPL3 Navigation > Off-Track Calculations and Track Marking > The One in Sixty Rule

Navigation paper 3 Q6 Answer B

The needle of the magnetic compass will try to align with the earth's magnetic field, and so it will 'dip' down as the magnetic field pulls down towards the magnetic pole as latitude increases. As 'dip' increases, so the compass becomes more prone to errors, and the magnetic compass is generally considered to be unreliable beyond about 70°of latitude.

Further Reference: PPL4 Aircraft General Knowledge > Instruments > The Magnetic Compass

Navigation paper 3 Q7 Answer A

The answer this question, it is necessary to know some simple definitions:

Flight Level (FL)	The altimeter reading when the altimeter 'sub scale' is set to 1013 hectopsacals (hPa).
Altitude	Vertical distance Above Mean Sea Level (AMSL), the altimeter reading when the altimeter 'sub scale' is set to QNH.
Height	Vertical distance above a fixed point on the surface, the altimeter reading when the altimeter 'sub scale' is set to QFE.

When the QNH is less than the 'Flight Level' setting (1013hPa), altitude will be less than the indicated flight level. The difference between Flight Level and altitude is found by the difference in pressure (hPa) x 30, because there are approximately 30ft per hPa.

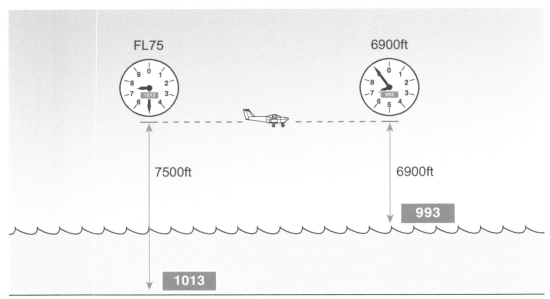

Thus, 1013hpa – 993hpa = 20hPa. 20 hPa x 30ft = 600ft. Therefore, when at FL75 (ie 7500ft with 1013hPa set on the altimeter), the aircraft's altitude is 600ft lower, which is 6900ft AMSL.

If the terrain directly beneath the aircraft has an elevation of 1400ft AMSL, the aircraft's height (above that terrain) is 6900ft – 1400ft = 5500ft.

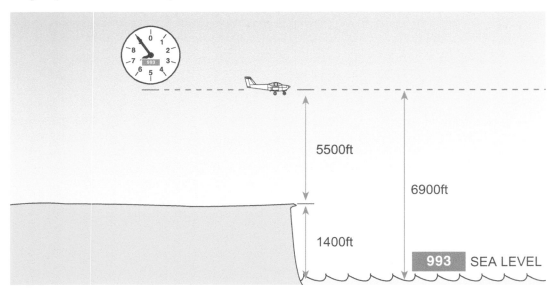

Further Reference: PPL3 Navigation > Vertical Navigation > Altimeter Settings

Navigation paper 3 Q8 Answer B

For a GPS receiver (also known as a GNSS receiver) to calculate a three dimensional position, it must be able to 'see' and receive signals from at least 4 satellites.

Further Reference: PPL3 Navigation > Radio Navigation > Global Positioning System (GPS)

Navigation paper 3 Q9 Answer D

The relevant 'Q' code definitions in relation to direction finding are:

QDM	The aircraft's **magnetic track to** the VDF station – the magnetic heading, if there was no wind, to take the aircraft to the VDF station
QDR	The aircraft's **magnetic track from** the VDF station
QUJ	The aircraft's **true track to** the VDF station.
QTE	The aircraft's **true track from** the VDF station.

Further Reference: PPL3 > Navigation > Radio Navigation > Ground Direction Finding (DF)

Navigation paper 3 Q10 Answer A

On its own, a Relative Bearing Indicator (RBI) only points to where the NDB is relative to the aircraft. This means that if an aircraft was tracking directly away from an NDB in conditions of nil drift, the needle would always point directly behind the aircraft (ie Relative Bearing 180°)

So, the aircraft's track is irrelevant to answering this question (it is already stated that the aircraft is tracking directly away from the NDB), all that counts is the drift.

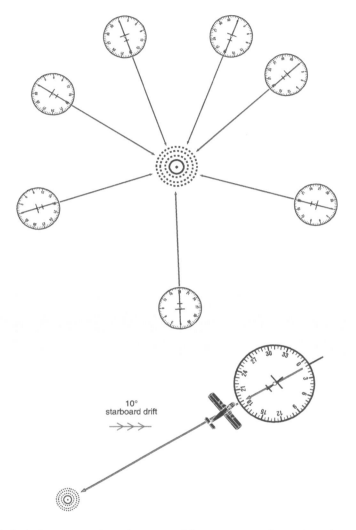

10°
starboard drift
⇒⇒⇒

Starboard (right) drift means that the aircraft's nose must be pointed to the left of track – in this case by 10°.

Further Reference: PPL3 > Navigation > Radio Navigation > Automatic Direction
                      Finding (ADF)

Navigation paper 3 Q11 Answer A

This can be remembered simply by knowing what the abbreviations 'VOR' and 'VDF' stand for, namely:

VOR	**VHF O**mni-directional **R**ange
VDF	**VHF D**irection **F**inding

For interest, SSR and DME operate in the Ultra High Frequency (UHF) band, and NDBs operate in the Low Frequency (LF) and Medium Frequency (MF) bands.

Radionavigation Aid	**Frequency band**
DME	UHF
NDB	LF & MF
SSR	UHF
VDF	VHF
VOR	VHF

Further Reference: PPL3 > Navigation > Radio Navigation > VHF Omni-directional Range

Navigation paper 3 Q12 Answer B

A VOR ground station transmits two signals, the aircraft's VOR receiver measures the phase difference between these two signals to establish the aircraft's magnetic bearing relative to the ground station.

Further Reference: PPL3 > Navigation > Radio Navigation > VHF Omni-directional Range (VOR)

Intentionally Left Blank

Paper 1					Paper 2					Paper 3			
	A	B	C	D		A	B	C	D		A	B	C	D
1	☐	☐	☐	☐	1	☐	☐	☐	☐	1	☐	☐	☐	☐
2	☐	☐	☐	☐	2	☐	☐	☐	☐	2	☐	☐	☐	☐
3	☐	☐	☐	☐	3	☐	☐	☐	☐	3	☐	☐	☐	☐
4	☐	☐	☐	☐	4	☐	☐	☐	☐	4	☐	☐	☐	☐
5	☐	☐	☐	☐	5	☐	☐	☐	☐	5	☐	☐	☐	☐
6	☐	☐	☐	☐	6	☐	☐	☐	☐	6	☐	☐	☐	☐
7	☐	☐	☐	☐	7	☐	☐	☐	☐	7	☐	☐	☐	☐
8	☐	☐	☐	☐	8	☐	☐	☐	☐	8	☐	☐	☐	☐
9	☐	☐	☐	☐	9	☐	☐	☐	☐	9	☐	☐	☐	☐
10	☐	☐	☐	☐	10	☐	☐	☐	☐	10	☐	☐	☐	☐
11	☐	☐	☐	☐	11	☐	☐	☐	☐	11	☐	☐	☐	☐
12	☐	☐	☐	☐	12	☐	☐	☐	☐	12	☐	☐	☐	☐

Answers

Intentionally Left Blank